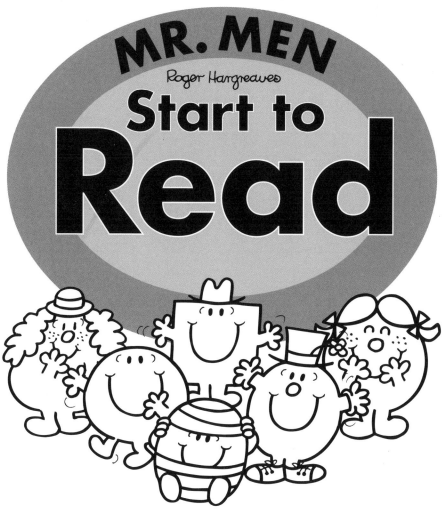

MR. MEN

Roger Hargreaves

Start to
Read

Illustrated by Adam Hargreaves

Exercises devised by John Malam

Educational consultant: Betty Root
Formerly Director of the Reading Centre

MR.MEN   LITTLE MISS
MR. MEN and LITTLE MISS™& © THOIP (a Chorion company)

Printed and published 2008 under licence from Price Stern Sloan Inc.,
Los Angeles. All rights reserved.

First published in Great Britain in 2004 by Dean, an imprint of Egmont UK Limited,
239 Kensington High Street, London W8 6SA

ISBN 978 0 6035 6264 8

5 7 9 10 8 6
Printed in Italy
www.mrmen.com

This is Mr Bump.
He's starting to read.

Draw lines to match the things that are the same.

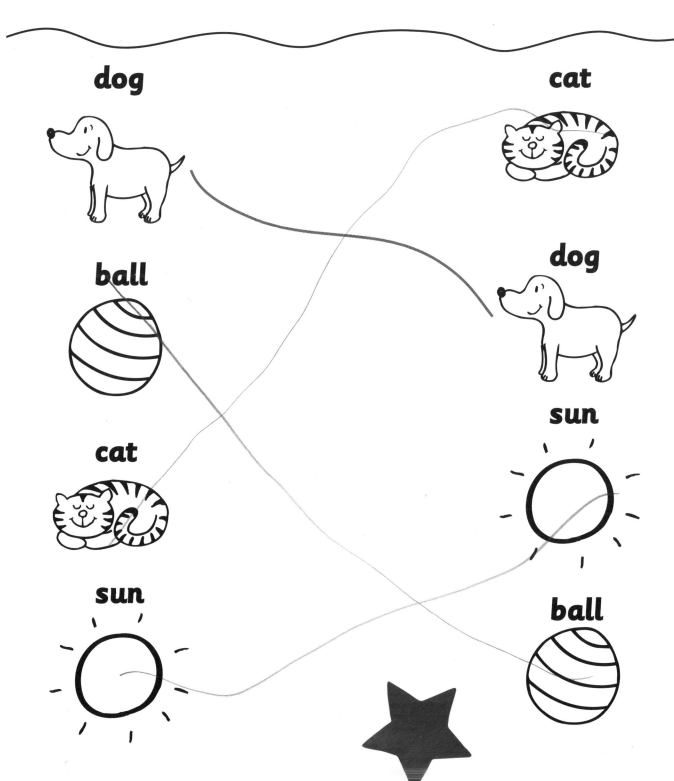

dog

cat

ball

dog

cat

sun

sun

ball

Help Mr Bump to find the
odd one out.

**Draw a circle around
the odd one out in each row.**

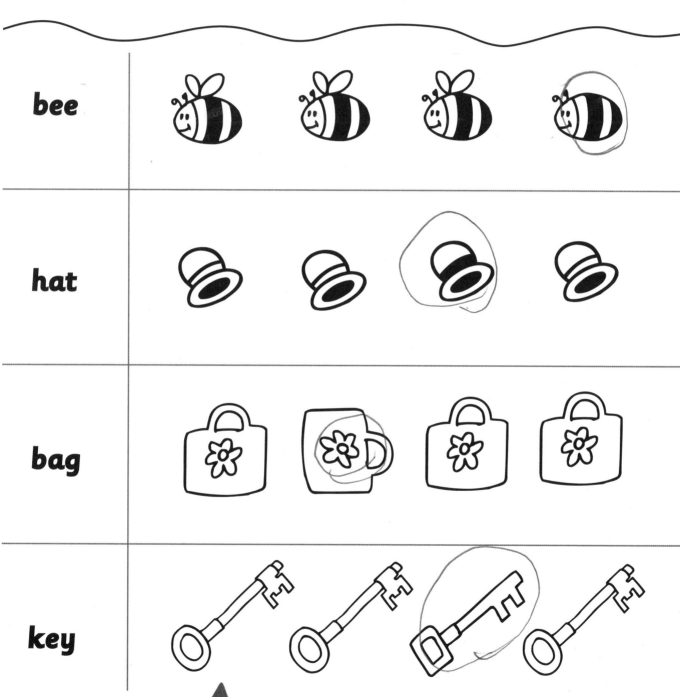

bee

hat

bag

key

This is Little Miss Sunshine.
She knows the letters in her name.

**Draw lines to match the letters that
are the same. The first one is done for you.**

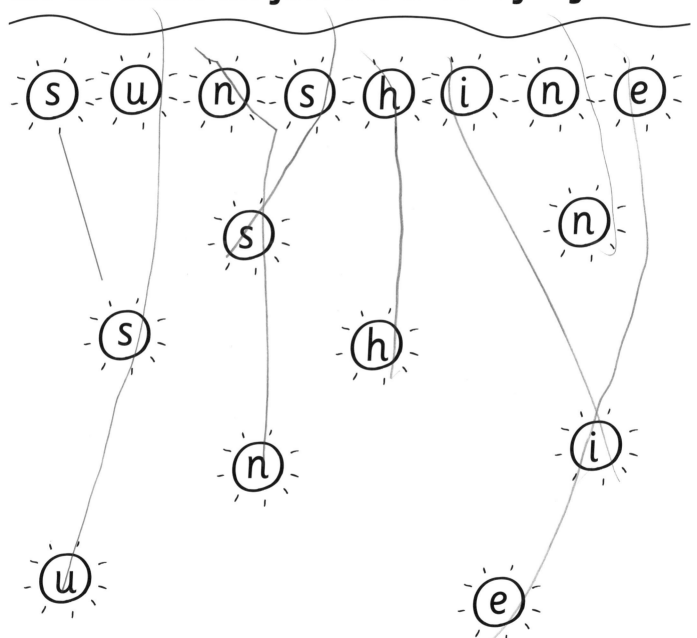

Write the name here s engfine

Little Miss Sunshine is flying her kite.
Find the objects below in the big picture and colour them in. Copy the words.

sun

flower

bird

tree

kite

This is Mr Noisy.
When he sings his mouth makes
the same shape as a letter O.

Draw a circle around each letter O.

O

o

e

e

e

e

e

o

e

o

o

How many letter O's did you find?

Mr Noisy is looking for some letters.

Look at the beginning sound of each picture. Circle the letters that are the same.

apple

a   a   c   a   e   a   o

orange

o   e   o   a   o   e   o

cat

c   a   c   o   c   c   a

sun

s   c   s   a   s   s   o

umbrella

u   n   i   u   a   u   u

This is Little Miss Splendid.
She has drawn this picture for
you to colour.
The letters tell you which
colours to use.

g = green b = blue r = red
y = yellow o = orange
Colour all the apples red.

**Here are some words to match.
Draw 3 lines between 3 words
that are the same.
The first one is done for you.**

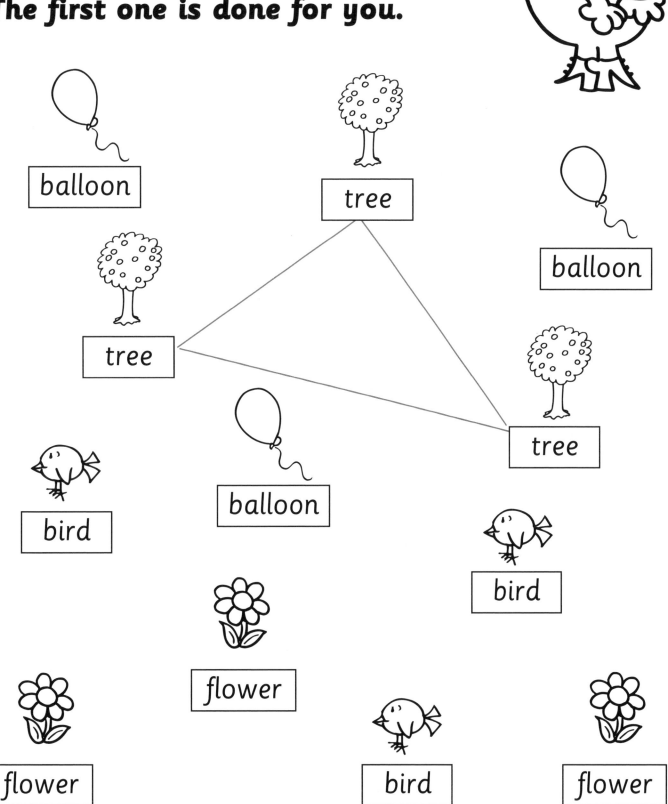

This is Mr Tall.
He is as tall as a very tall tree.

Draw a circle around each letter t.

tree

How many did you find?

Draw a circle around the odd one out in each row.

table

tiger

tent

teapot

This is Little Miss Busy.
She is busy reading.

Help her match each picture to its correct letter sound.

f is for

s is for

h is for

t is for

<u>s</u>un

<u>h</u>at

<u>t</u>ent

<u>f</u>ox

Little Miss Busy is in the park.

Find the objects below in the picture and colour them in.

1 sun   **2** trees   **3** balls   **4** hats   **5** flowers

This is Mr Tickle.
He is reaching for the letters
on the shelves.

Draw a circle around the odd one out on each shelf.

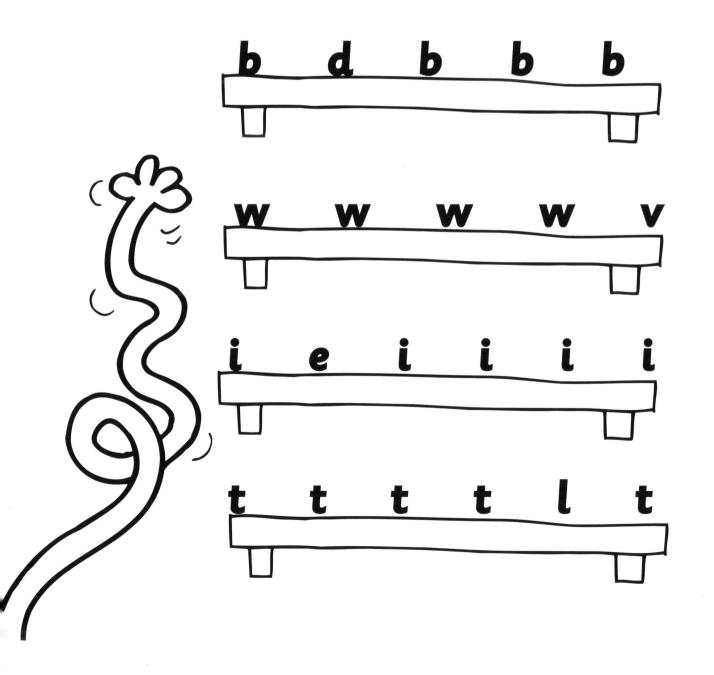

b   d   b   b   b

w   w   w   w   v

i   e   i   i   i   i

t   t   t   t   l   t

Help Mr Tickle match each picture to its correct letter sound.

a is for

dog

e is for

watch

d is for

apple

W is for

egg

This is Little Miss Helpful.
She likes to help, but sometimes
she's not helpful at all.
Look what happened when
she did some painting.
Tell the story from the pictures.
Then draw what you think happens next.

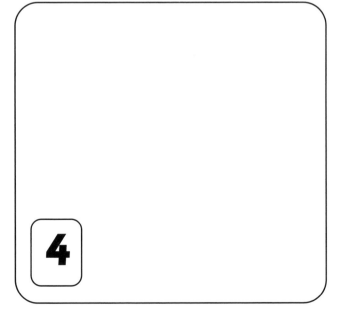

Little Miss Helpful is looking at these pictures.

Help her to join the pictures which begin with the same sound.

This is Mr Small.
He is on holiday.
Colour the picture. The letters
tell you which colours to use.

g = green   y = yellow

Look at the word on the left. Then find the word that is the same along the line. Draw a circle around it.

fish	frog	fish	four	flower
sock	sail	soap	sock	seal
watch	worm	wall	watch	wheel
boat	boat	bird	belt	bags

This is Little Miss Tiny.
She's learning about letter sounds.
You can too.

Match each picture to its correct letter sound.

n *is for*

j *is for*

r *is for*

g *is for*

u *is for*

Little Miss Tiny is as tiny as a mouse.

**Find the tiny letters in the picture and circle them.
How many did you find?**

This is Mr Nosey.
He wants to find the way to
Mr Messy's house.

**Join the letters of the alphabet to
find the correct path through the trees.**

a b c d e f g h i j k l m

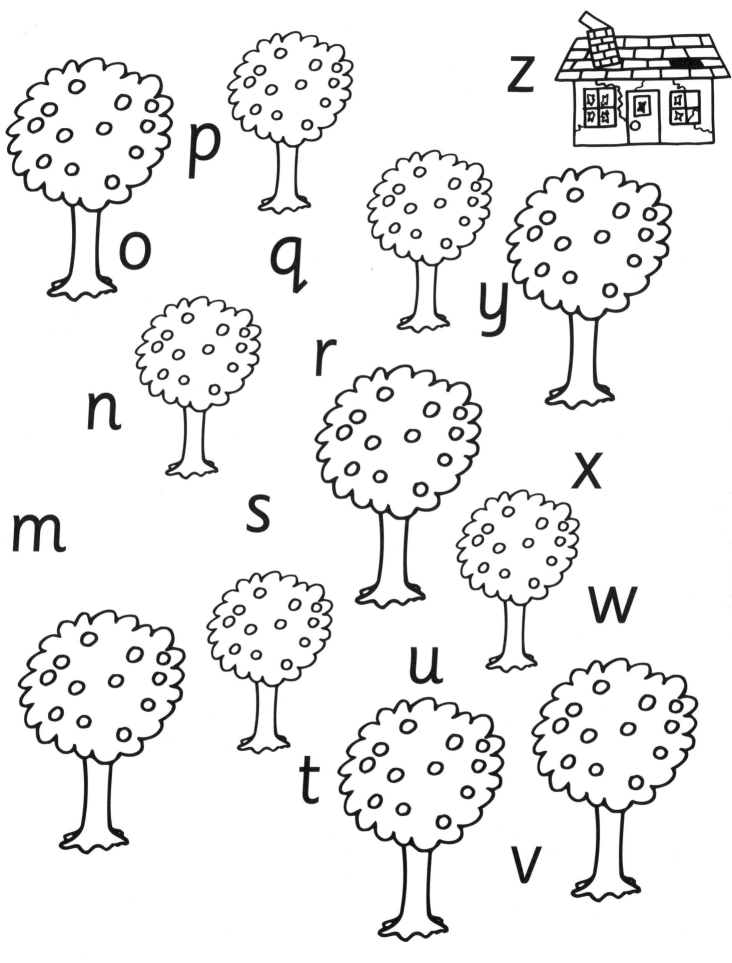

o p q r n m s r y x w u t v z

n o p q r s t u v w x y z

Notes to parents

Get a good start with the Mr Men.

This book is part of a series designed to prepare children for starting school. The following skills are covered in this book:

• observation;

• story telling;

• recognising letter shapes;

• connecting these letters with the sounds they represent.

The aim is to build confidence and make learning as much fun as possible. By working on these activities with your child you can offer help and encouragement, and share the fun. Here are a few simple ways that you can help your child to learn.

• Start at the beginning of the book and work through each page. The activities get gradually more difficult, building on what your child has learnt.

• Short sessions are more likely to hold your child's interest, so do not try to do too much in one go. You might start with just one activity. Stop if your child is losing concentration or an activity seems too difficult; you can always come back to it later.

• Be sure to reward your child's efforts. If your child feels successful, he/she will be keen to learn next time.

• Discuss each activity with your child to make certain that it is understood before any writing takes place. Asking questions and puzzling out the activities together is an important part of the learning process.

Note: Tell your child the sounds of the letters as well as the letter names. For example, say "buh" not "bee" for the letter b.